STRESS-FREE CHICKEN TRACTOR PLANS

2nd Edition

Step-by-Step Instructions

By John Suscovich

EMERALD LAKE
BOOKS

Stress-Free Chicken Tractor Plans

Copyright © 2016 Farm Marketing Solutions, LLC

Cover design by Gerber Studio
gerberstudio.com

Books published by Emerald Lake Books may be ordered through booksellers or by contacting:

Emerald Lake Books
emeraldlakebooks.com
860-946-0544

ISBN: 978-0-9965674-8-0 (pb)
        978-0-9965674-9-7 (ePub)
        978-0-9971207-0-7 (pdf)

Library of Congress Control Number: 2016950975

Printed in the United States of America

PRAISE FOR
STRESS-FREE CHICKEN TRACTOR PLANS

Best chicken tractor design ever!

I can't say enough good things about this chicken tractor design, John really did his homework. It's well worth the price, read it twice and build it.

- Diane P., Amazon reviewer

Thorough and practical

This book has help make Chicken Pasturing enjoyable. The well thought-out process and clear instructions of building the tractor made this a leisurely weekend project. The helpful insights to using the tractor (feeder, waterer, moving, etc.) have all been implemented and have been real time savers! Great book!

- Jim Q., Amazon reviewer

Was a quick read with lots of great insight and information. Well written with helpful drawings and firsthand experience instruction.

- L. Lenox, Amazon reviewer

Super sturdy chicken tractor plans with great user instructions

I highly recommend John's *Stress-Free Chicken Tractor Plans* if you want to build a sturdy, long-lasting chicken tractor. Mine has held up perfectly for over three years now and is outside full-time, winter through summer. We've raised Cornish Cross birds, Red Isa's and even ducks in it.

- Joe S., Amazon reviewer

Best book for chickens!!

John is awesome. This book is simple, precise and easy to follow. I watch his YouTube videos and he has taught me a lot. It's a great book and very useful if you have a lot of land or very little.

- Brandy, Amazon reviewer

Excellent

Quick and easy to follow read with great info and illustrations. The tractors are the best looking and most functional I have seen thus far. Watching John's YouTube videos inspired me to purchase this and start raising our own chickens! Whether you are competent when it comes to construction or not, this book has easy step-by-step instructions and even a shopping list, so all the guesswork is taken out of the process. Thank you, John, and keep up the good work!

- Moe, Amazon reviewer

Don't search any farther. This is the best tractor you will make.

The title says it all. I bought the plans about 14 months ago and have ran about 200 birds through our pastures with this chicken tractor. The plans are super-detailed, easy to read, and a fantastic finished product. Take the time and do the half-lap joints. It makes a ridged frame. Ours has gone through over a year in North Texas. Once during a winter storm (no chickens present), it was blown over and tumbled about 100 feet. All we had to do was turn it over and it was good to go. (Remove the tarp when not in use. It eliminates tractor crashes.) You will gain more than just a chicken tractor with this book. John's keen insights as a holistic chicken farmer and animal lover comes through on every page.

- Daniel Brubaker, Amazon reviewer

A must-have book if you plan on pasture raising poultry!

I cannot recommend this book enough! I met John several years ago and fell in love with his chicken and the way he raised them. Fast forward a few years and I found myself owning a large farm and there was no question in my mind that I would build his tractors and follow his plan. We planned out our year and built three tractors in the spring. By mid-summer we had built three more. We had a very successful broiler year using these plans. My morning chores were so easy to do by myself. The tractors were also a big hit with our customers. When they see the attention to detail, it really shows how well the chickens are being cared for. These tractors quickly became a topic of conversations around town. Not only does this book lay out everything needed to build the tractors, it includes invaluable information regarding pasture rotation, feed, predators and all the other little questions that come with deciding to raise pastured poultry. If you are thinking of building a chicken tractor, this book is a must have!

- Heather Holland, Amazon reviewer

Great design, great book!

...Being a handyman/farmer/carpenter myself I was skeptical of how much I would really be getting out of [John's] designs. However, I was extremely pleased with how detailed and easy-to-follow his instructions were, as well as his comprehensive discussion of all things related to successfully raising meat birds. I thoroughly enjoyed it, have no regrets and would buy it again! Can't recommend it enough!

- Amazon customer review

Very well written with many extras and generally just a good solid plan!

- Ron McConnell, Amazon reviewer

No need to learn the hard way. John already did that for us!

As a wannabe, beginning farmer, these plans helped me get off on the right foot as I started raising poultry on pasture. After building three chicken tractors and having them perform great over a season, I am thrilled and see why it's called the "stress-free" plan. Through John's own trial and error, I was able to benefit by not having to go through the same issues that he did as he figured things out. He did a lot of the work for us and for that I am very grateful. The design is excellent and the plans are easy to follow. Having built a Salatin-style tractor in the past, I would HIGHLY recommend going with this one instead. It's actually portable (as in you can move it with a trailer to new locations if necessary), looks great and is WAY easier to move. This book helped me get my start as a farmer and I will continue to use the plans as I expand in the future. Thank you, John, for all of the work and dedication you've put into this!

-Jay, Amazon reviewer

Top-notch chicken tractor design, plus priceless pastured poultry experience

John Suscovich's design is top-notch. His experience in raising pastured poultry is priceless. This book, the YouTube videos, and his website are incredible resources for small (and not-so-small) pastured poultry producers. We produced 65 meat birds in our startup year and currently have a flock of 130 healthy, happy birds. We used information from the first version of Stress-Free Chicken Tractor Plans to improve the portability of our hoop coops and to streamline our operations. Chickens are an integral part of our (non-certified) organic vegetable farm, and John Sucovich's materials have been an inspiring and informative influence on our success.

- Wyman-in-Colorado

This is a great book! To put it simply, John has perfected the chicken tractor. Not being a carpenter and having built my own chicken tractors previously, I can assure you John's plans are the best. My tractors were too heavy and consequently hard to move to fresh grass. John's design, with the wheels added to the relatively light-weight frame, makes the necessary chore of moving the tractor easy. So, feel confident about building John's stress-free chicken tractor plans. You won't regret your decision.

- Jennifer W., Amazon reviewer

I've had some form of chicken tractor or mobile coop for the past 6 years all with their fair share of challenges. John has created a system that is not only economical, but safe from predation and most importantly fast to use. I have two of these tractors on farm and my daily moves are faster, safer and easier on the birds and my back. I will be using these plans exclusively as I continue to take order for my budding pastured chicken CSA grows. This book is a bargain at twice the price.

- Amazon customer review

Detailed, Illustrated, Thoroughly Explained

If you can't build your chicken tractor from these plans with these instructions, I just don't know what to tell you. The plans are well thought-out, detailed and thorough. The illustrations make anything that might be confusing completely clear. The text explains the reasons everything was chosen, and why a particular method was used.

If you want to build a chicken tractor, this is what you need for instructions.

- Amazon customer review

Excellent design. Well presented and easy to follow. The multi-use functionality (chicken tractor, cold frame/greenhouse, pastured layers, etc.) of this design makes it ideal for those of us managing a smaller amount of land. I recommend with no reservation whatsoever.

For Kate and Mabel.

CONTENTS

FOREWORD

It seems that raising poultry can either inspire passion or thoughts of pain. It generally elicits very strong feelings in people, often dependent on their management practices.

For a while, I fell in the pain camp, especially when my family first started raising poultry without much capital, infrastructure or feeding and watering systems. However, after a few years of tinkering, building, tearing down and rebuilding again, we developed a system of mobile coops, waterers, feeders and portable fencing that worked for us.

Once we dialed in those systems, our pastured egg-laying and broiler flocks became relatively easy and profitable additions to our farm that didn't take hours of daily chores.

This book you have in your hands can save you a few years of pain by going directly to a system of raising meat birds that has been proven by farmer and educator John Suscovich. John has a passion for sharing his ideas, both trials and tribulations, with a wider circle of farmers and would-be farmers. He wants to see small farms succeed and thrive.

I too share this passion and wrote a couple books on similar subjects myself, *Farms with a Future: Creating and Growing a Sustainable Farm Business* (2012, Chelsea Green Publishing) and *The New Livestock Farmer: The Business of Raising and Selling Ethical Meat* (2015, Chelsea Green Publishing). I figure if I could glean the best wisdom from other sustainable farmers around the country and tie in some of the lessons that I learned farming with my family, that I could maybe save other people from making similar mistakes and move closer toward success.

Stress-Free Chicken Tractor Plans is a concise and practical book that covers so many of the important details when building and deploying mobile chicken shelters. Our broiler chicken shelters were very similar to John's design. Ours were just a tad bit bigger and used thicker skids instead of wheels. We even bent metal conduit pipes just like John does for the roof.

I'm sure that many other inventive farmers around the country have built similar structures because they make sense, are strong yet light enough to pull, and are economical and can serve multiple purposes (love the kid shelter idea!).

Thanks to John for taking the time to explain his pen design as well as feeding, watering, moving and predator control systems.

If you raise chickens or are thinking about it, you will find this book a handy addition to your bookshelf.

Rebecca Thistlethwaite
Farm & Sustainability Consultant and
Author of *Farms with a Future* and *The New Livestock Farmer*

THE BEGINNING OF A JOURNEY

Raising broiler chickens can be fun, rewarding and profitable. There is a night-and-day difference in the quality of life and richness of taste between a chicken raised on pasture, eating grass and bugs, versus a chicken you would buy in the store. Without a doubt, the difference comes from the grass, and that's something you cannot recreate in a barn.

Depending on who you are, chickens may be your friends, your food, your passion or your business. You have to keep them safe from predators and happy with their living arrangements, while giving them access to forage.

Yet the whole situation has to be enjoyable for you as well. To keep your chickens safe and happy, you are going to need a chicken tractor design that works for you. The tractors described in these plans were designed and built by me and for me, but after seeing hundreds of pictures of other people using this design, I know it works for others as well.

These tractors were designed for broiler chickens. As you will read in this book, though, they have several other uses as well. My daughter loves using them as forts. A friend of mine is using them as a hutch to raise rabbits. Another homesteader keeps a few egg-laying chickens in them seasonally. They're pretty useful for whatever you can imagine.

In this book, you will find more than the professionally drafted chicken tractor plans. You will find information on how to build them, what materials I used and why, as well as how to build your own feeders and waterers.

Since I was starting my farm on a tight budget, all the materials and design elements were chosen to cut costs without sacrificing structural integrity or animal welfare. As the saying goes, "poor guys can only afford the best." I knew I would only have enough money to build these once and couldn't afford to spend time fixing them. That is why I had to get it right from the start.

I can now say, years later, that they are holding up strong with almost no defects aside from what can be attributed to normal wear and tear.

This is a guide for anyone from a small-scale backyard homesteader to a full-production poultry grower. These tractors will hold up to 30 chickens each. Not only will they provide a good life to the chicken, but a good life to the farmer as well. I have used these same chicken tractors to raise up to 2,400 broilers in one season.

I wrote this book so that you could have answers to all of the questions I asked when I was starting out.

My Own Journey – Then and Now

When I first wrote this book, life was insane. My wife, Kate, and I had bicycled 5,500 miles across the country, finished a season apprenticing on a farm, and decided to take the plunge and start our own farm. On top of all that, Kate was pregnant with Mabel, we had to buy a car, move to a new town, and Kate got a teaching job.

It was simply too much to take on in one year and, without the support of friends and family, combined with many sleepless nights, we would have never been able to pull it off.

At the end of that season in 2013, I got a job as the farm manager at Camps Road Farm where I am today. Along the way, I have made a lot of mistakes, learned even more, and have come to enjoy the process in ways that I never have before.

I started farming 100% on my own at my FoodCyclist Farm. I started out with just 1,300 broilers and a small herb garden on someone else's land with a handshake lease. I now live on and manage a 52-acre farm with livestock, annual and perennial plants, and two other directly connected businesses—a brewery and distillery.

Life is just as insane as it was when Kate and I started out on our own, but in so many better and more interesting ways.

In this book, you'll read about both when I started out and how I do things now. While the broiler operation is fundamentally the same as it was in the beginning in terms of type of management and scale, I have become more solid in my practices, more nuanced in my decisions, and more confident as a pastured poultry producer.

When you're starting out, you're going to be super-nervous. Even if you do a small batch of broilers, that's 25-30 chickens you have to care for, keep alive and then—well—kill.

The first time you raise broilers, it's going to change how you view chicken. It's going to be amazing, a little stressful and a boatload of enjoyable. After a few seasons, you're going to be an expert and you'll wonder what life was ever like without the best chicken you've ever eaten.

As You Explore, Question Everything

Or at least take it with a grain of salt.

One of the early traps I fell into with farming caused many hard times for me. The problem was, I assumed everything I read was fact and that I should follow it. There is as much bad information out there as there is good ol' scientific fact, which is an exhausting aspect of small-scale farming today.

Some homesteader or small-scale farmer will make claims on their blog or YouTube channel about how to raise chickens, livestock or crops a certain way because "you have to." I have been guilty myself of making a claim based on half-science and then I had to go back and create another video recounting my advice because I had done more research.

In the world of the internet, bulls*** can be spread with the best of intentions.

Another pitfall is, while there may be scientifically accurate advice for a certain person in a certain region, that doesn't mean it is going to work for you in your situation. It may or may not be a fact that is adaptable to you.

That is the true art of farming—patience, intelligence and an acceptance of living the process. As farmers, we take the advice and information that we gather from our various sources and we iterate, experiment and take notes. Simply by the nature of its existence, a small diversified farm will run thousands of experiments a year.

The longer I farm, the more I am challenged. I keep gathering new information, experimenting on my farm and developing my process to suit my skill level, goals and motivations. While I'll let you be the judge as to whether or not I am actually a smart feller, I do feel that as time goes on my questions are becoming more specific, more intelligent and constantly lead to more questions on how I can improve my process.

If you truly like raising chickens or you just want agriculture in your life somehow, I encourage you to always question the advice of internet farmer geeks like me. We love what we do and our content may be born from real fact, but always do your own research, read academic studies and talk to your extension officers. The world is a fascinating place and there is always something more to learn. Farming will teach you a lot if you are patient, listen, do your own tests and are willing to adapt.

BEFORE YOU GET STARTED

Woodworking Skills for Building Chicken Tractors

One of the things I have tried to do with this book is to not only show you how to build my chicken tractors, but to give you some light carpentry skills. A basic understanding of how a few power tools work combined with a certain level of comfort with carpentry and construction will prove to be valuable on your farm.

I don't know about you, but I learn best by doing. I figured I had an opportunity here to teach you a few carpentry skills in the context of building a chicken tractor. It's fun and I hope you don't mind expanding your horizons a bit.

Why This Design? Is It Right for You?

When I was starting out, I spent a lot of time designing my chicken tractors. I have traveled to farms across the United States seeing for myself how other people raise chickens in addition to a variety of other farm business models.

Since becoming a poultry farmer and starting Farm Marketing Solutions (FMS), I have had the pleasure of being in contact with many more farmers through my Growing Farms Podcast and the FMS YouTube videos. Their influence, thorough research and my own needs and resources all played a part in how I settled on my design.

When I first started my research, the most popular chicken tractor design was created by Joel Salatin of Polyface Farm and is detailed in his book, *Pastured Poultry Profit$*.

I have to admit, Joel and his writing have been a huge influence in my life. I honestly don't know that I would have become a poultry farmer if it were not for him. So I was eager to do whatever it was that he told me I had to do to be a successful poultry farmer.

Joel's tractor design is a good one. Farmers across the country have raised hundreds of thousands of chickens in them. However, it was not a design that was going to work for me. I actually built one of his tractors, but took it apart when I realized it was just not a good fit.

When I failed at the Salatin-style chicken tractors, I went back to the drawing board. And by "the drawing board," I mean searched on Google Images for "chicken tractors." I just couldn't find anything that I liked specifically, but I did find several designs that had different elements that I liked. Drawing from my design background, I Frankensteined all the parts together and built the chicken tractors that I've been happy with for several years now.

Will this design work for you?

Well, you saw the pictures and video, and you bought the book, so something about it rang true to you.

My advice if you're just starting out with raising chickens is to build just one chicken tractor and plan to raise 1 or 2 batches of chickens for the first year. You want to make sure that you actually like the design and the process of raising chickens before you go and build 24 of them like I have on my farm. If you like it, build more. If you find problems, then you haven't invested too much in it.

Why Make Chicken Tractors Mobile?

When I was starting my farm, I knew I might not be there forever because I was leasing land on a handshake. I also had to use several different fields in different locations. My apartment was in one place, the carpenter's shop in another, and the pasture in yet another. I was all over the place, but this is what I had to do to make everything work.

Fast forward a few years and I now manage a 52-acre farm. Much of that farm gets soaking wet at certain times of the year. I don't have any long flat fields where I can raise one batch of chickens after another. At times, I have to move the chicken tractors from one end of the farm to the other.

Since the chicken tractors were built to be mobile and fit in my landscaping trailer, it's easy to move them. I designed them with portability in mind.

My initial farm car was a Honda Pilot, which is a large SUV. I love my car and think it is possibly one of the best cars you can get for farm work. With the versatility of an SUV and the towing capacity of a small truck, there isn't much I haven't been able to do with my Pilot.

Given that my SUV didn't have a truck bed, I purchased a 6' x 12' landscaping trailer. The trailer has a ramp that folds down in the back and 1' side rails. Next to my Pilot, this is my most important piece of farm equipment.

Knowing I'd need to transport the tractors from place to place in between batches of chickens and that my handy landscaping trailer measured 6' x 12', I used the trailer for the chicken tractor footprint. They are sized to be a few inches smaller on all sides than my trailer for "easy on, easy off" handling.

Years later, I can tow that same trailer with my ATV now, so I'm not compacting the pasture that much when I need to pull the trailer. I use it for chicken tractors, moving processing equipment, and transporting chickens to processing.

I have since stopped using the Pilot as my farm car because I am no longer the only person working on my farm. The farm now owns a GMC Sierra 2500HD, a ¾-ton pickup truck. I love having a truck for the farm. The truck bed means I don't always have to resort to towing the trailer when I want to move something, and the bigger engine means I can tow more when needed.

The right vehicle for your farm is a decision you'll have to make for yourself. That's a conversation for a whole other book, but what I want you to think about is where these chicken tractors are going to live during the season and over the winter when they're not in use. Think about how you'd move them, how you'd store them, and let some of that guide your decision-making.

Understanding the Math Behind a Chicken CSA

One enterprise that my farm engages in is our Chicken CSA. "CSA" stands for "Community Supported Agriculture." Members buy a share for the season up-front and get product throughout the season, as it becomes available. This is more popular with vegetable farms, but poultry farmers can do it too. I raise chickens both for a CSA and for individual retail sales at the farmers' market or our farm store.

My CSA members get one chicken every week for 20 weeks during the season for a full share. Half-share members get a chicken every other week for 20 weeks (in other words, they get 10 chickens). And the CSA season runs from the beginning of June to the end of October.

With a footprint of about 60 sq. ft., I could put 30 birds in each tractor and remain within the certified humane standards. I found that roughly 28-30 birds per tractor is a good number for this design.

For the first year of the FoodCyclist Farm, I processed 60 birds a week for CSA and farm sales. I would have 120 chicks delivered every two weeks throughout the season, so that my rotations kept my chicken tractors full once I started processing birds.

One batch of 120 chicks will give me two weeks of meat processing. That means 4 tractors for each batch of 120 birds. (120 birds ÷ 30 birds per tractor = 4 tractors needed.)

I kept 12 chicken tractors in production throughout the season and raised roughly 1,300 birds that first year.

My current model has me processing once a month instead of once a week because I decided to supply a frozen product. Now the farm isn't centered around poultry, but poultry still is a big part of the farm. To cut back the hours I had invested in chickens, I began making bigger batches with fewer rotations.

Now I get 240 birds delivered once a month. I also have the whole batch processed off-site at a USDA-inspected facility each month. By moving to a frozen product, I was able to gain back brooder time, processing days, and cut down on management.

In short, more birds gave me back my time. Now I'll raise about 1,200 birds in a season with less time spent on poultry, which allows me to focus on other projects.

As of the writing of this book, there is a new processing facility opening much closer to my farm. This might completely change my chicken batch rotations. If you want to keep current on developments during my farm seasons, then visit me at FarmMarketingSolutions.com or YouTube.com/Farm-Marketing.

Scaling Up

The chicken tractors in this book are built for the homestead to small-scale producer. One of the things to consider if you're thinking about raising 10,000 chickens a year, is just how many of these chicken tractors you would have to build.

Honestly, that would be insane. These tractors fit in a niche within a niche. They are great if you're just starting up or if you plan to stay "small." (Pastured poultry is a great side operation to a farm business and these things get the job done. So, it doesn't need to be the primary focus of your farm.)

I have raised up to 2,400 broilers in one season using 24 chicken tractors. That was a big summer for moving livestock. My staff and I were pretty tired by the end of it. On top of the broilers, we had egg-layers, crops, fruits and sheep.

If I were to go that big again or if I wanted to scale up to a more serious number of 5,000 or more, then I would think about redesigning the chicken tractors to be a little bigger. I would also need more land, too.

When I'm considering adding a new chicken tractor, the formula I use is 35 days on grass multiplied by the footprint of the chicken tractor (which is 60 sq. ft.).

So, for a single tractor, I need a minimum of 2,100 sq. ft.

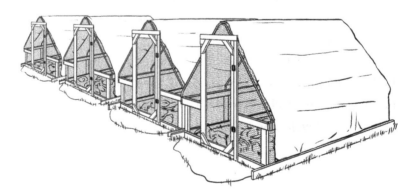

Farming Alone

Another obstacle I was facing early on was that I was the only person taking care of the daily operations of the farm. That means I had to build, transport to pasture, and move these chicken tractors every single day by myself.

One person *can* build these, though two is preferable. With the wheels on, I can load them on and off my trailer by myself. And I can move all of them by myself every day.

I don't mention this because I am proud of doing it on my own. Well, I am a little... But mostly, it's because I wanted to illustrate that this design can be mobile and, if absolutely necessary, you can do it with one person.

That being said, make friends with someone and share the chores. It is so much better.

Other Uses for These Structures

Another reason why I settled on this design was because it's versatile. This is not a meat bird-only design like Joel's. With some very simple modifications, you can use these tractors for several other areas around the farm.

- Egg-laying hens
- Rabbits
- Turkeys
- A cold frame for small garden beds or starting some seeds early
- A kick-a** fort for your kids (Mabel loves playing in them).

With the 2'-high frame that makes up the base, you can easily add on a few nest boxes and use the tractors for pastured eggs. You will have to put fewer chickens in each tractor, but if you are a backyard grower with no need for a large flock, it could be perfect.

You might want to have a more solid coop for the winter and use this to range the birds during the summer months when the grass is growing. I will let you know, though–this structure is not suitable for winter housing for egg birds.

These tractors are heavy enough not to blow around, but light enough that two strong people could lift it between them. With the addition of some aluminum channel and wiggle wire along the bottom rails, you could easily add on greenhouse plastic and turn your chicken tractor into a cold frame.

Since raising broilers is more of a seasonal operation, this allows you to either extend the season for your birds or extend the life of your garden further into the colder weather by wheeling the tractor over to a vegetable patch that you started in the summer or fall.

If all else fails, you can make sure there are no sharp edges and use them as some really cool mobile forts for your kids. Since we live on our farm year-round and we rotate batches of chickens, there tends to always be an empty chicken tractor around somewhere. My daughter, Mabel, loves to use them as a pretend house. She invites Kate and I in for imaginary food, and she occasionally locks us in there. I've also seen the neighborhood kids use it for a home base for games of tag.

CHOOSING A CHICKEN TRACTOR DESIGN

As I designed my chicken tractors, I had three main factors in mind.

- Form
- Function
- Cost-efficiency.

For it to be a good fit for me, it had to hit on all three points. It'll be the same for you. So know what it is that you're looking for, and keep looking until you find it.

Form and Function

I have seen a lot of rough-looking chicken tractors in my travels and research. Nothing wrong with that, it's just not my style. I have to look at these things every day, and I like things neat and tidy.

My tractors had to look slick for two reasons. One, I had to impress myself so that I would be happy showing up to work every day. Entrepreneurship is a constant emotional battle and how you feel about your work environment will greatly affect how well you perform your tasks. If you enjoy going to work, you will get more done and you will live a happier life.

More importantly, I had to impress my new customer base. I was a guy starting a chicken farm from scratch in a town where I had just moved. Selling people on a vegetable CSA is easy compared to selling people on the idea of getting a chicken a week for 20 weeks. I needed people to see my chicken tractors all laid out and say, "Wow!"

When my chickens tractors are lined up on pasture, people pull over on the side of the road to stop and look. I love it. I always invite people to come check out the chickens.

"This is where your food comes from."

It's not hard to convert an interested party into a buying customer once they've seen the care you put into raising your chickens.

While I wanted my chicken tractors to look good, I could not throw function out in the name of aesthetics. I raised over 1,300 chickens during my first year of owning and operating my farm. With at least 480 chickens on the farm at any given point and a host of other projects to get done, I had to get in, do my work and move on as quickly and efficiently as possible without sacrificing quality of life for my birds.

I built these tractors so that feeding is easy, getting water to them is easy, and there is very little in terms of any other maintenance. The design is also rugged enough to stand up to strong winds, predators and other sorts of nasty weather.

I had a list of demands I worked out at the beginning of the design that I wanted to meet.

A key thing for me is that I wanted to be able to stand up in my tractors when gathering chickens. The design here is about 5' 5" inside, which is a little too short for me, but it's close enough for comfort.

I also wanted a really good shelter for the birds while providing adequate air-flow.

When you're designing your farm or homestead, my advice is to look at everything with two lenses. The first lens is *function*. The second is *form*.

Function is more important than form because you need to get the job done effectively.

However, I also think that it is important to keep a clean farm and put some effort into the aesthetics of the place. A clean and orderly farm is an efficient and effective farm. You will get more done, it'll be easier to manage people (both employees and customers), and you will enjoy being there more because where you are is beautiful.

Cost-Efficiency

Simply put, my budget was limited. It still is.

All of the materials I opted to use were chosen to save money without sacrificing on quality or durability. With an average cost of about $200 to put each chicken tractor together, they're a really good deal considering how long they will last.

I get an amazing amount of stuff done on the farm. I have to. With regard to the infrastructure of your farm, if you need to use something, it has to work every single time.

When the harvest is ready to come in or you are getting ready for poultry processing, everything has to work because you don't have time to deal with huge headaches or to make mistakes.

When you cut corners to be cheap, you lose money in the long run. The more time you spend chasing down and fixing all the things that go wrong because you cut corners, the less time you will have to do the things that will make you money. We call that, "penny wise, pound foolish."

Even while rewriting this book, I have a list of things that have broken on my farm that I now have to fix. It's unavoidable that things will break, but it can be mitigated by making the decision to go with the better materials and properly caring for your tools.

Not everything I own is brand new. In fact, it rarely is. But I take care of my things. Everything gets put away in its place, everything is maintained, oiled and given the care it needs. I am in no way saying you should go out and purchase the best-of-the-best tools. Sometimes cheap is the only option you have and that is okay. A shop full of quality tools is something acquired over a lifetime.

For these chicken tractors, there is cheaper hardware you can use, there is cheaper lumber, and there are probably cheaper tarps. I'm sure there are also ways to cut corners that I didn't even think of. The thing is, it took me some time to build all 12 of my first tractors. That is time I won't get back and a task I honestly don't want to relive for a while.

I want my tractors to last as long as possible and that's why I chose the materials I did.

GETTING STARTED

Tools Required

Circular Saw

Cordless Drill

Speed (or Tri-angle) Square

Tape Measure

T50 Hand Stapler or Pneumatic Staple Gun with Narrow Crown Staples

Wood Chisel

Pencil

Conduit Bender

List

Material	Quantity
2" x 4" x 12' pressure-treated wood	3
2" x 4" x 10' pressure-treated wood	3
2" x 4" x 8' pressure-treated wood	2
1" x 4" x 8' pressure-treated wood	4
½" hardware cloth	2' x 35'
1" chicken wire	4' x 35'
½" EMT conduit (Electrical Metallic Tubing)	5
90° gusset angle	4
9" Simpson strap tie	1
8" cable ties	Large bag
½" x 6" galvanized carriage bolt (axle)	2
½" nuts and washers for carriage bolt (axle)	2 of each
3" hinges	2
Barrel bolt latch	1
10' x 14' white tarp	1
⅜" braided cord	20'
Wood glue	1 bottle
2½" Torx wood decking painted screws	1 box
1¼" Torx wood decking painted screws	1 box
9" cart wheel	2
5-gallon bucket (*optional*)	1
Chicken nipple drinkers (*optional*)	5

MATERIAL CHOICES EXPLAINED

As you looked over the shopping list, you may have wondered to yourself, *Why did John make that choice?* or *What if I used x instead?*

Let me explain a little bit why I chose the specific items I did. If you want to do something different, that's completely up to you, but at least you'll understand the rationale behind my decisions, and perhaps have enough information to make your own informed decision as well.

Wood

I got my lumber and most of my materials from Home Depot. It's a "big box" store where they sell just about anything you would want for home repair and improvement. They usually have what you need and the price is typically pretty good.

It takes some digging to find lumber that is not curved, bent, checked, cupped, knotty or messed up in some way. I took my time and sorted through the lumber to find the pieces I wanted. Working with twisted lumber is not only extremely frustrating, but it makes for inaccuracies as well. The 1" x 4"s are especially hard to find good pieces. Take your time to sort through the wood. It is worth the extra effort!

I used pressure-treated wood for all of my construction on this project. I wanted these tractors to last. After all, they are a major investment of time and money, and I didn't want to have them rot and fall apart in three years.

Chicken Wire

I say this as a poultry farmer who loves what he does. I hate chicken wire, plain and simple.

Well, I guess I just dislike building with it. Once it's in place, it's really not a bother and it is pretty good at what it does. It gets the job done. For most of the chicken tractor, I went with your standard 1" mesh chicken wire purchased at Home Depot in long rolls.

Having gone a few seasons with only the chicken wire on the bottom, I have to say that, if I were you, I'd do the upgrade suggested in this book.

For the bottom two feet of the chicken tractor, I would now use ½" hardware cloth instead of chicken wire. The tighter wire on the bottom will help keep predators from reaching inside the chicken tractor with their grubby paws.

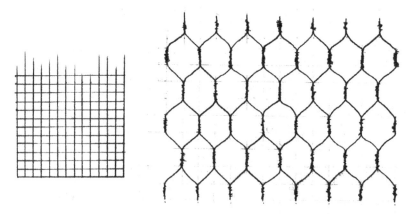

With the 1" spacing of the chicken wire, a raccoon could still get its paws between the mesh and injure your birds even if it doesn't kill them. Using either the ½" hardware cloth or putting up an electric wire around your chicken tractors will solve that problem.

Another option I have seen people use on chicken tractors is the plastic mesh. It is so much nicer to work with. Wire mesh rips up your hands and has a mind of its own, as it keeps trying to roll up and lose its shape. I stuck with the wire, though, because the plastic is generally much more expensive and I had a dozen tractors to build. It is also significantly less durable.

As with most things on your chicken tractor, the wire mesh is open to interpretation. You can use whatever combination of materials that works for you.

½" EMT Conduit

This has been a tough thing for most people to adapt to with the building of these tractors. I want you to feel free to use something else for your chicken tractors. There is no single right way to do it. As long as your birds are happy and healthy, that is all that really matters. That being said, here's why I went with conduit.

Found in the electrical section of the hardware store, ½" EMT comes in 10' lengths. You're going to bend four of them for the frame and leave one straight for the spine of the roof.

I chose ½" EMT because it would give me the durability that I wanted so that the roof of the chicken tractor would stand up, not only to strong winds and weather, but to the test of time as well.

The conduit is made to be able to bend and I was able to make the custom shapes that I wanted without too much effort or material. That also gave me the shape I wanted without having to attach several things together. Joints are usually the weak spots in a structure and, if I were to build it out of wood, then I would have a structure that was less sturdy and would have more potential points of failure.

I also like the low profile of the conduit material. It makes for a strong roof without having to use a lot of materials. The more material you have, the more it eats into the open space in the tractor. Remember, you're going to have to move around in it as you feed, water and catch your chickens. So it just makes sense to leave yourself as much open space inside as possible.

I had an old pipe bender at my disposal to bend the EMT. I bent a 90° angle in the middle and two 45° angles on either end leaving 3½" straight on the ends to fasten to the wood. This particular step in building the chicken tractor has given people difficulty in the past and I am hoping that the updated instructions on how to bend the conduit solves that problem. Just be warned that bending conduit can be a little tricky if you've never done it before.

As a possible substitution, you could just build the arch out of wood. Changes in the materials may result in slightly different chicken wire dimensions, so keep that in mind if you do decide to experiment.

You could also use plastic conduit or tubing if you have it available. That might be a little easier to work with. The reason that I didn't go with the plastic pipe is that it breaks down over time and at ½" there's not a lot of material there for structure.

90° Gusset Angle

I had considered using 2" x 4" to add in 45° cross-bracing

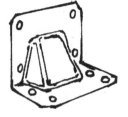

supports to add support and stiffness to the wooden frame. Looking at the front and back of the tractor where the board comes into contact with the ground, that's where the most wear and tear is going to be. You're dragging it across the ground. Even with the chicken tractor raised on wheels, occasionally you're going to snag on a rock or a bunch of sedge grass or some other obstruction on pasture and I thought it prudent to build up those two ends of the tractor.

Instead of adding more wood to the frame and thus more weight, I used 90° metal gusset angles that I bought at the hardware store. They are in the section where all the hardware for building decks is. These braces on each corner add rigidity and extra support as you pull the tractors around on pasture.

If you don't want to buy the metal ones, I do suggest cutting a piece of wood to create a 45° angle to add support against lateral torsion and the wear and tear discussed above.

Cable Ties

I went back and forth on how I was going to fasten the chicken wire to the frame. I even started out re-using the wire that comes wrapped around the chicken wire rolls. That was awful to work with because metal is always stiffer and having to tie all those pieces of wire quickly got tedious.

I like using the cable ties, or "zip ties," because you can get the zip tie through the loops in the wire and pull it tight without having to tie knots or worry about twisting wire. I used the heavy duty 8" black cable ties to secure the chicken wire as well as to secure the tarps on the tractor. I space the ties 8 to 12" apart depending on where I am on the tractor.

The chicken wire that is going to be covered by a tarp doesn't need as many ties because there really isn't going to be anything trying to break in there. At the front and back ends of the tractor, I put the zip ties closer together because that's where a break-in might occur.

When you're attaching the zip ties to put the chicken wire on top of the chicken tractor, do it while you are inside so that the tails are inside the chicken tractor. I ended up cutting the tails off of the ties so that they wouldn't hit me when I was working in the chicken tractor.

I had a friend help me build some chicken tractors and he fastened the zip ties onto the roof pieces standing on the outside of the tractor, not working from the inside. He also cut the tails and that's where our problem came about. With the cut plastic pieces facing outwards, they rubbed on the inside of the tarps when the chicken tractors were set up for the season, which wore holes in the tarps that now would either have to be repaired or replaced.

Every fall, when I am closing down the farm for the winter, I just cut the zip ties holding the tarps on and fold up the tarps and store them for the winter. As for the zip ties holding the chicken wire on, I have left them in place for four years as of the writing of the second edition of this book. I really haven't had any break on me. If one falls off, I just replace it with a new tie.

I'm sure they're all going to start breaking at some point, in which case I'll just take some time and go through and replace them all. After spending 365 days a year outside, the plastic may become brittle and break. Considering how cheap it is for a zillion zip ties versus how useful they are, I deem them a very worthwhile expense.

Carriage Bolts, Washers and Nuts

Having only one pair of wheels that slides on and off each tractor is very efficient. While I didn't want to buy wheels for every single chicken tractor, I do keep a set with each batch of chicken tractors. I looked for a wheel/axle combination that would work well together and get the job done.

For the axles, I used the 8" galvanized ½" carriage bolts that are used on decking. In fact, they are in the decking section of Home Depot. In the same area, you'll find the washers and nuts. You will need one washer and one nut for each bolt. The ½" bolts are sturdy and do not bend under pressure.

With the kind of weight and the nature of the use of these chicken tractors, you're going to have a hard time bending those bolts. The wood breaks before the bolts do.

I like the carriage bolts for a few different reasons. The head of the bolt sinks into the wood while you're tightening it, so you only need one wrench to install it.

That same end of the bolt is also flanged out, so that it acts as a washer holding onto a larger surface area of the wood for added support. They are also rounded on top, so you're not going to snag them on anything when you're moving the chicken tractors around.

For these, I went with the thick galvanized bolts because I didn't want them to rust.

9" Strap

I bought a 9" strap for each tractor. These straps are again found in the decking section of the hardware store. It is a 1" x 9" galvanized metal strip. They have a ½" hole that fits around your ½" bolt and several smaller holes that you can put screws through.

When you put your carriage bolts through the back legs of your chicken tractor and put the wheels on, in time the inside edge of that wood will start to loosen up and the wheels

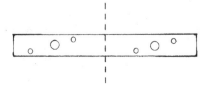

will start to wiggle. That little wiggle is an issue because over time it is making the wood around it weaker.

The outside edge that holds the top of the bolt typically has no issues.

I solved the wiggle problem by reinforcing the wood on the inside of the chicken tractor leg. Put the strap on and screw it down before you put on the washer and nut.

I cut the straps in half because I only needed half for each side. I used a pair of tin snips to cut the strap. You can either use the same straps that I used or find an equivalent replacement.

Hinges

I looked for simple inexpensive hinges that would not rust. I ended up with a 3" hinge that I can get for a couple dollars each.

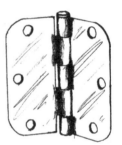

If I had a little more cash, I might have chosen a hinge that had a spring on it to shut the door behind me. A self-closing door would be pretty sweet, and maybe that's something you'd like to consider for your chicken tractor.

Latches

I have used a couple different latches through the years and the one I mention in the directions is hands down my favorite. The sliding pin latch works well to keep the door shut

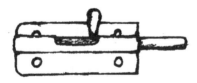

and, if you don't put the second part of the latch on the door, you can just keep the door shut by sliding the bolt into the frame.

Screws

Are you using cheap Phillips head screws? Stop it! Anything you are taking the time to screw instead of nail, you want to last and hold up to whatever you happen to throw at it. I glue all my joints first, but the screws do a lot of the holding. So, get good screws.

Generic coarse-thread drywall screws stink. Drywall screws have decent pull strength, but cannot take much lateral torsion.

What does that mean? Try to pull it straight out and it will be tough. Try to twist the two pieces of wood and it will break.

Your tractors are going to twist and bend a lot (believe me) and you don't want your joints popping apart with sharp bits of rusty screw hanging out all over the place.

They also rust over time and are not recommended for use with pressure-treated lumber.

The screws I use everywhere on my farm are Torx wood  decking painted screws. They are a "Torx" or "star" drive, which is the least likely to strip or "cam" out. They are much stronger than the less expensive drywall screws and can take more of a beating. Not only that, but they're less likely to rust due to the polymer coating.

I keep several sizes on my farm at all times. They're something like $10 a pound for a box of them, but I have found them to be worth the price. Since the Torx head is not likely to strip, if there is anything that I am taking apart, I can easily get the screws out.

Tarps

The size of the tarp I recommend for my chicken tractor design is 10' x 14'. This covers the length of chicken tractor and the width over the top.

I chose to use tarps for the chicken tractors for a few reasons. First off, they are cheaper, lighter and easier to find than a lot of other materials.

I thought about using metal or plastic corrugated roofing panels, but they are just not readily available in my area and when you do find them they're pretty costly. I found the tarps cover more area for a better price.

Another thing that I liked about using the tarps is that they are seamless. I had started to build a chicken tractor with some of that roofing that I got off Craigslist, but I was worried about how to overlap it, not only to fit the size I wanted, but to make sure as little rain got through as possible. The tarps provide an easy-to-install seamless roofing solution.

In the beginning, I had tarps that didn't go all the way to the ground on all sides. I still use some of those, but I am phasing them out. Those were 9' x 12'.

Since then I have moved to fitting the chicken tractor with the exact size tarp that it needs, which is 10' x 14'. Having the tarp go down to the ground on the two long sides gives the birds better protection, not only from bad weather, but from predators as well. There is still plenty of ventilation with the ends open and if need be I can always roll them up.

The last thing I'll note about the tarps I chose is the color. White tarps are the best for chicken tractors. When the summer sun is beating down, the white tarps help to reflect some of the intensity of the sun's rays, keeping the chickens cooler.

I also looked for UV-resistant tarps. It seems that the sun is only getting stronger and these chicken tractors are going to be outside all summer long. Having white UV-resistant tarps is good for the birds and makes the tarps last a little longer.

Wood Glue

I glued all of the joints on my wooden frame. I wanted these to last, so it was glue and screw for the whole thing. I just used a standard exterior wood glue for the joints.

Use it liberally—better a little too much than too little. The glue not only helps hold the wood together, but it fills in any cracks or gaps you might have.

Wheels

I use 9" wheels on the tractors. That gives me a roughly 3" clearance between the ground and the bottom of the chicken tractor when they're attached.

The wheels that you use will depend on your area and what is available to you. A couple things to look for when you're wheel shopping...

All plastic wheels will start to mar or get misshapen on the inside causing the bolt to bind as you're putting the wheels on or taking them off. Not that it always happens, but it has happened to me.

Metal wheels where the bearings are pressed into the rest of the wheel can fail as well. Over time, the bearings work themselves out and either fall into your pasture to be lost forever or into your hand and you're left wondering what to do.

I ended up buying the metal wheels and tack-welding the bearings in place into the rest of the wheel. However, I know this solution isn't for everyone. You'll have to make the best decision for your circumstances based on what's available. Don't be afraid to ask for help from the clerk at your favorite hardware store.

Rope

To tie up the feeders and waterers, I used ¼" nylon braided rope. You can also use ¼" rope. I chose a synthetic rope so it won't rot, and braided rope so it won't slip and drop whatever it's holding.

For the handles on the chicken tractors, I used ½" nylon rope. I didn't use braided rope for this as the thicker rope tends to hold a lot better. Over the ropes, I recommend putting an 18" piece of garden hose or 1" well line so that, when you pull the rope, it doesn't hurt your hands as much.

STEP-BY-STEP INSTRUCTIONS

I'm going to provide the list twice. First, without commentary, then in greater detail. Once you've built your first chicken tractor, you may find it easier to use this page as a simple reminder, rather than reading through all the details again. Either way, here we go!

1. Gather your materials.
2. Cut everything you need to the right lengths.
3. Cut all of the half-lap joints.
4. Assemble and join the sides.
5. Celebrate!
6. Bend and attach the conduit.
7. Attach the chicken wire.
8. Celebrate again!
9. Add the finishing touches.
    a. Gussets
    b. Rope
10. Add a waterer.
11. Add a feeder.
12. Cover it with tarp.
13. Install the wheels.
14. Celebrate one last time. Your chicken tractor is done!

Now to dive deeper into each of these steps.

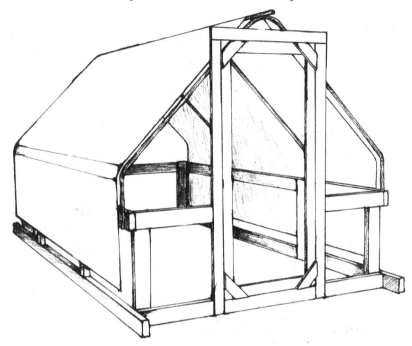

Step 1. Gather Your Materials

First things first, we need some materials to build with. If you haven't read the materials explanation before this, I recommend reading through it before you go shopping. It could save you some heartache down the road.

Step 2. Cut Everything

After we have gathered our materials and done our shopping, it's time to move on to the cut list.

For the cut list, we're starting to prepare all the pieces we're going to need to assemble our chicken tractor. When I am building something, I almost always cut all my raw materials to length first so that when it comes to assembly I can just put the whole thing together.

Here are all of the parts you're going to need.

Part A: Cut one 2" x 4" x 8' board into four 2' sections.

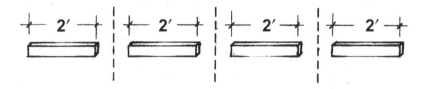

Part B: Cut another 2" x 4" x 8' board into four 2' sections. Yes, they're the same length as Part A, but they are used differently. And don't worry if the last piece is a bit short. It's a chicken tractor after all and the length of that particular piece isn't critical.

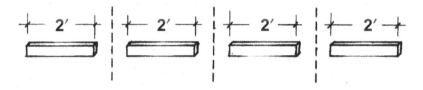

Part C: Cut one 2" x 4" x 12' board into two sections, both 5' 7" long.

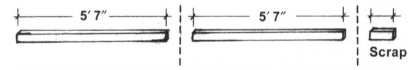

Part D: Just leave two 2" x 4" x 10' boards whole.

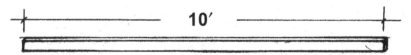

That was easy, wasn't it? I thought I'd give you a break after those first cuts. Success!

Part E: To create the bottom rails of the chicken tractor, cut two of your 2" x 4" x 12' boards into 11' 4" lengths.

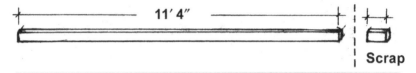

Parts F & G: Cut one 2" x 4" x 10' board into one section 5' 7" long for Part F and, with the remaining wood, cut two sections 1' 9⅜" long for Part G.

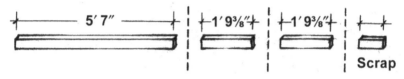

Parts I & J: Cut two 1" x 4" x 8' boards into one section 4' 8½" long for Part I and one more section 2' long for Part J. You're cutting two of the same size board the same length. That way, you'll end up with two of each of these parts.

Parts K & L: Cut two 1" x 4" x 8' board into one 5' section for Part K and one more section 2' 7¼" long for Part L. Once again, you're cutting two of the same size boards the same length, so that you end up with two of everything.

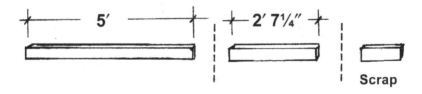

Step 3. Cut the Half-Lap Joints

This image shows you the result we're going for with half-lap joints. What we're doing is removing some material from two pieces of wood to make identical opposing notches. Those notches will then fit together and be glued and screwed in place.

I chose to use half-lap joints because they add a lot of structural integrity and flexibility, which I feel is worth the extra effort. This allows the chicken tractor to conform to the ground a little better, while still holding up to the rigors of farm use.

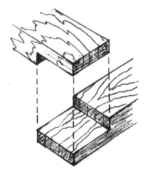

If you like, you can skip the joints and simply screw the pieces of wood together. Just keep in mind that doing so will affect some of your measurements and I don't account for that in this book. I have a strong leaning toward putting in the effort and making the half-lap joints, but of course you're welcome to do what you're most comfortable with.

Now that you know what we're shooting for, I'm going to walk you through an easy way to create half-lap joints using basic power tools and then I will give you all the measurements you're going to need for this chicken tractor.

This is an intermediate woodworking technique, but I have faith in you. You're going to learn something cool here if you didn't already know how to do it. Having honed my technique on my chicken tractors, I now use it elsewhere on other carpentry projects around the farm.

To create a half-lap joint, set your circular saw blade to a depth of ¾". Each 2" x 4" piece of lumber is actually 1½" thick, not 2". We want our cuts to remove half of the thickness of the wood. Setting the blade depth ahead of time ensures we take off the right amount of material.

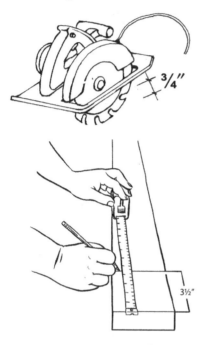

Measure the area that you are going to remove with your saw cuts. For the most part, we are joining 2" x 4" wood with 2" x 4" wood. So the actual measurement is 3½".

After you make your cut, you can double-check it to make sure it's wide enough by holding up a scrap piece of 2" x 4" to the cut to see if it fits together properly. If it's not wide enough, you'll have to cut a bit more.

Use your speed square to make the first lines to give you the boundaries for where you're going to cut out your notch. You can then shift the speed square over a little bit to act as a guide for the saw. Speed squares come with a lip that you can place flush against the nearest edge of the board. Holding that there, line your saw up with the mark you made and cut the first line.

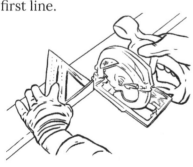

Once you know the area that you're going to work in, you can then make several cuts next to each other within the bounds of your intended joint. You're removing a bunch of material here, but don't worry about cutting all of it off with the saw. Just space your cuts ⅛" to ¼" apart.

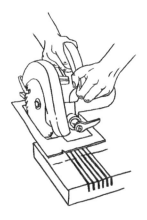

Your board will start to take on a striped pattern. When it does, take a hammer and tap on the pieces. They will fall out in little chunks.

After you have gotten out what you can by just tapping it with the hammer, go back and clean it up with a wood chisel. Alternatively, you could just keep the saw running and move it back and forth over the joint to clean up the excess here.

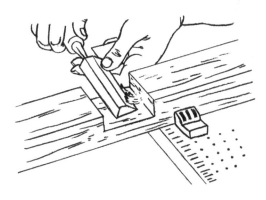

It doesn't have to be perfect, but we do want to knock down any big ridges that are going to make it so the joints don't sit flush together.

Our final result will be two pieces that fit cleanly together to create a strong joint.

Half-Lap Joint Measurements

Now that you know how to make the half-lap joints, here are the measurements.

You're going to take the parts that you cut in Step 2 and position the joints as shown below.

Part A: x 4

2′

3½″   **3½″**

Part D: x 2

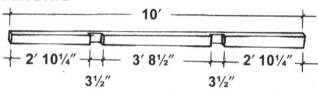

10′

2′ 10¼″   **3′ 8½″**   **2′ 10¼″**

3½″   **3½″**

Part E: x 2

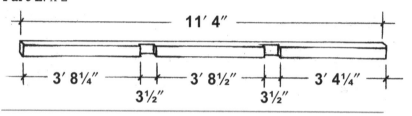

11′ 4″

3′ 8¼″   **3′ 8½″**   **3′ 4¼″**

3½″   **3½″**

Part F: x 1

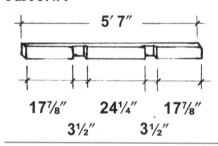

5′ 7″

17⅞″   **24¼″**   **17⅞″**

3½″   **3½″**

Part G: x 2

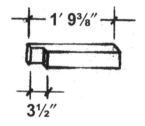

1′ 9⅜″

3½″

You'll get into a rhythm while making these cuts. It'll seem a little daunting at first and then you'll become more comfortable and settle into it. You'll be done before you know it.

If you work in a team, I recommend having one person measuring and doing the chisel work and the other person cutting with the saw. It helps a lot.

Step 4. Start Putting it Together

Match up the pieces following the picture that follows.

As mentioned earlier, when you assemble the pieces, it's best if you glue them first and then screw them together for added strength.

You'll want to pay particular attention to the screw pattern you use as well, since improperly assembling your chicken tractor will shorten its useful lifespan.

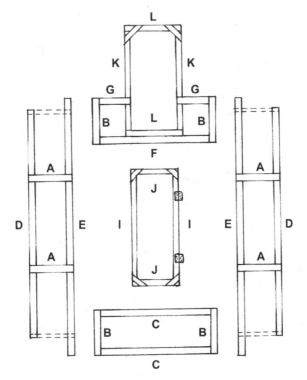

Screw Pattern

Wood grain on lumber tends to go in one direction. You can see it when you look at a board—it's fairly easy to tell which direction the grain goes.

What we want to do with our screw pattern is make sure no two screws end up along the same line in the grain. If your screws are positioned along the same line, your wood is more likely to split because you're gradually wedging it apart.

Take a look at the image. You can see that none of those

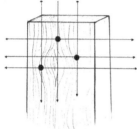

lines match up. Not only that, if you're connecting two boards together, none of those lines are going to match up on the other piece of wood either.

This is the screw pattern to use for maximum strength.

Once your sides are together, you can put the whole frame together. The detail below shows you how the pieces of wood come together at the corners and then how the conduit will be attached.

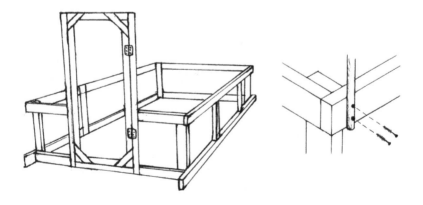

Step 5. Celebrate!

Step 6. Prepare the Conduit for the Roof

Bending the conduit can be a little tricky. It took me some time to get used to, but once I had it, I was able to crank out roofs for chicken tractors quickly.

This isn't the most exact science, but you can get close. Don't fret if you're off by an inch or two on your bends. It's a chicken tractor, you'll be fine.

Let's start by measuring where we are going to make those bends.

Conduit comes in 10' lengths. Measure your center line 5' from the end of the conduit.

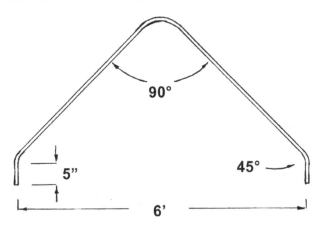

When bending ½" conduit, you're going to need a 5" offset for your bend to land in the center. So measure 5" from your center line in either direction and make a mark.

A quick way to measure all four at once is to lay them all out on a flat surface. Line all the ends straight against a scrap piece of wood. That way, when you measure the first one, you can take your speed square and mark all four at the same time.

Once you've marked all the places, go back and hold your pencil on the mark you made and roll the pipe along the surface of the table or bench you're on. That marks the pipe all the way around. It makes your life a little easier for the next steps.

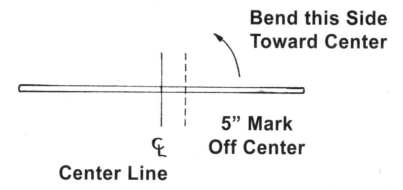

Bend this Side Toward Center

5" Mark Off Center

℄

Center Line

Line up your mark with the arrow on the bender as shown and bend the conduit back toward your center line until the pipe makes a 90° angle. The conduit bender stops at 90°, so you cannot over-bend it.

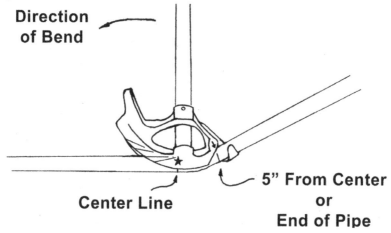

Direction of Bend

Center Line

5" From Center or End of Pipe

Once you have all four of your 90° bends, it's time to make a jig. This allows you to line up you conduit so that all the bends

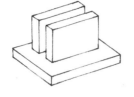

are in the same direction. It's simply two boards screwed to a third board with a gap wide enough to sandwich my conduit in between. I put the 90° bend right into that jig and one leg of the pipe stands up in the air while the other rests on the ground. I put my pipe bender on the end that is resting on the ground and bend my 45° angle in toward the 90° angle so they are lined up.

I then rotate the piece of conduit and do the other side so it matches.

When placed on the ends of the pipe to bend the 45° angles, the conduit bender is automatically going to give you about a 5"-long straight piece.

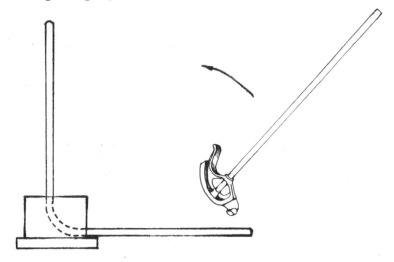

After you have all the bends made and your metal is starting to look like a roof, it is time to move on to pre-drilling the holes for the screws. You can skip this step by using self-drilling screws, if you prefer.

The conduit is attached to the base of the tractor with the same screws I used on the wood frame. I pre-drilled two holes through the metal to fit the screws through. Be careful when you are drilling through the conduit. The drill bits will have a tendency to break if you're not holding the bit straight.

To help hold the conduit while I drilled into it for my screw holes, I built a little jig that sits on a picnic table. I used a couple scrap pieces of 2" x 4" and made the shape you see pictured here.

The little notch held the conduit and the piece on the

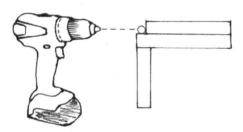

bottom helped brace against the edge of the table to let me lean into the drill a little bit.

The top spine of the roof is only held on with zip ties. I crisscrossed two zip ties in each place where the top pipe crossed one of the arches. Between that, the chicken wire and the tarp, it holds great.

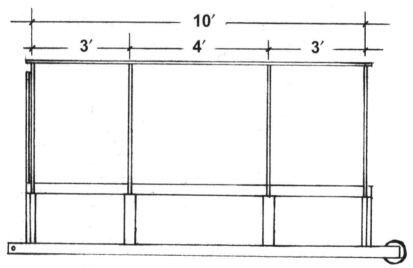

Step 7. Attach the Chicken Wire

Once the whole frame is put together, it's time for chicken wire. You may choose to use another type of wire on your chicken tractor as I talk about in "Material Choices Explained" on page 21. No matter what you choose, I strongly recommend two things.

The first goes back to the beginning, don't go it alone. Get another person. Chicken wire is awful. It constantly wants to roll back up and an extra set of hands is priceless.

The second tip is to get yourself a pneumatic stapler with good staples. You can put the chicken tractor together with a cheaper T50 hand stapler, but the wire won't be as secure.

I used a pneumatic stapler with narrow crown staples to secure the wire to the wood. That adds a lot of durability when it comes to a bobcat pulling on the chicken wire to get in. Trust me, read the chapter called "Predators" on page 69.

To secure the wire to the conduit, I used 8" black zip ties. Placing them about every 6 to 8" along the pipe will keep the wire secure and the predators out. I have seen a hawk trying to get in and the ties held. They also let you get the wire pretty tight as you cinch them up. I periodically check on them and replace them as they wear out.

The chicken wire pattern I have detailed here (*next page*) is just one way to do it. But it's based on my experience with what I've built already and what I would do differently if I were to do it over.

In my original plans, I used 1" chicken wire over the whole thing. You can still choose to do that, but you'll just have to buy more than I have specified in the materials list.

The new configuration has chicken wire starting higher up on the tractor and uses ½" hardware cloth around the base. It is safer for the birds and that was the focus.

You'll also note that I left a hole in the middle of the roof. That gets covered by the tarp and there is no way to get in through that opening. If you feel uncomfortable about it, just stick ten more feet of chicken wire over the middle and fasten it down to cover the hole. No big deal.

One final note... I used the ½" hardware cloth for the door as well. You can use chicken wire instead, of course. It's up to you. But the materials list assumes you'll be using hardware cloth too. So if you want to use chicken wire, buy more!

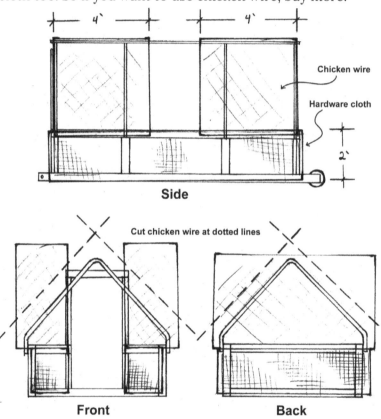

Side

Front   **Back**

Step 8. Celebrate again!

Step 9. Add the Finishing Touches

After you have everything assembled, you're on to the finishing touches for the tractor—the last step before moving to the feeder and waterer.

Gussets

Let's start by adding gussets to the chicken tractor. A "gusset" is just a bracket that strengthens an angle of a structure.

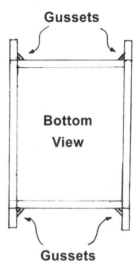

The gussets that you purchased go on the outside corners of the chicken tractor as I have pictured here. These metal angle brackets add rigidity and durability for pulling the chicken tractor through pasture.

Use four 1¼" screws to attach the gussets to the frame.

Rope

In the front of the chicken tractor, drill one ½" hole on each side to pass the rope handle through. Really wiggle that drill bit around in there. It makes it easier to get the rope through, depending on the thickness of the rope.

You may wish to take an old piece of garden hose and pass the rope through it to help preserve your hands when moving the tractor. I also have used 1" well line. The more rigid plastic is nicer on the hands.

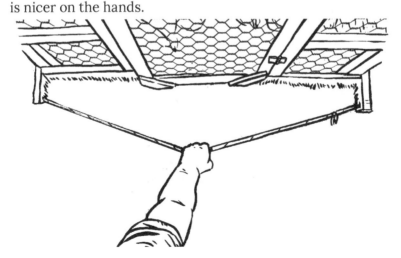

Tie the rope so you can grab it with your arms straight and your knees slightly bent. You want it so that when you straighten your legs, the rope picks the tractor up about 3" off of the ground and all you have to do is lean backward to move it.

While it's hard to say how easy it will be for you to move a tractor, my wife, Kate, was able to do it while she was 8 months pregnant. And my mother-in-law did the same after my daughter was born. So, while I wouldn't send a young kid out to move the tractor on their own, it should be fairly easy for the average person to do.

To make the handle easy to adjust for people of different heights, tie a bowline on one side of the chicken tractor to anchor the rope to that side. On the other side, tie a taught line hitch once you've passed the rope through so that you can adjust the knot depending on who is doing chores that morning.

Three Knots You Need for Farming

Having grown up as a Boy Scout and an avid camper and backpacker, knots were a big part of my life. I can pack a car full of camping gear like a professional, as well as secure it all with the right knots, if need be.

With all the knots that I knew at one point, there have been three that really stand out as useful for everyday farm life.

- Bowline
- Taut line hitch
- Clove hitch

I use these knots to tie up the trellis in the hopyard, hang chicken feeders and waterers, secure a load of stuff on a trailer, etc. They are just plain good to know in general.

Follow the diagrams below to see how to make each of these knots.

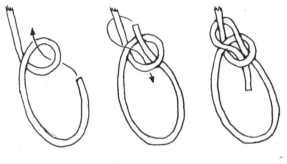

Bowline

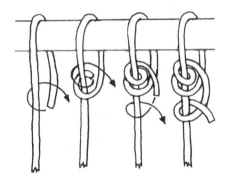

Taut Line Hitch

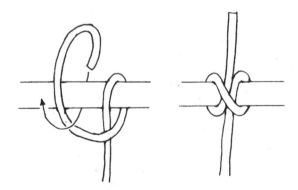

Clove Hitch

Step 10. Add a Waterer

This is something I still go back and forth on today. I have found a system that works for me for now, but you can bet I will still be looking for ways to improve.

I start the season using five-gallon buckets with chicken nipple drinkers drilled into the bottom. The recommendation is to have 10 birds to one watering nipple. In the case of chickens, it is always better to over-do it with access to water.

My chicken tractor design can hold 30 birds, giving each bird about 2 square feet of space. If you adhere to the 10:1 ratio for waterers, using four should cover you when the birds are smaller and the weather is not too hot. But, as with everything else in farming, there are variables. I typically use 5 drinkers per bucket to be safe.

The original design of my chicken tractors used hooks and a chain to suspend the buckets from the back of the tractor. Now I just suspend the bucket on a rope from the ridge line of the chickens' tractor because it cuts down on the wood used and it's a little easier to adjust. You can go with either method.

As the chickens are growing, I watch the level of the bucket. You want the birds to stretch their necks up a bit to get to the water. You don't want to have them stretch to extremes, though, as that's not good for them. I always adjust the height of the waterer for the smallest birds. The big birds do just fine.

You can train the chicks when they're in the brooder to use these drinkers so that when they move to pasture there's no disruption in how they get water.

Some Variables to Consider

I leave the tops off the five-gallon buckets so that I can easily refill them from the back of the tractor.

Unfortunately, with the tops off, "stuff" inevitably gets into the water. Whether it is bugs, dust or algae, you're going to get things in your water.

This presents a real problem when it starts plugging up your drinkers. That is why I suggest a few extras just in case. The birds will figure out which ones are working until you can take them down and clean them.

Whether there's stuff in the water or not, you must clean the waterers throughout the season. Like any chicken watering system, it is not a "set it and forget it" system. Even closed systems grow stuff after a while and it is good not only for the efficiency and effectiveness of the waterer, but also for the bird's health, that you keep the water clean.

When the temperatures climb into the 90s and above, the nipple drinkers are just not enough. If you're raising Cornish rock cross birds especially, the heat stresses them out and that leads to death.

Water Solution for High Temperatures

Chickens do not sweat. They pant.

When temperatures climb, they pant so fast and so hard that they become stressed out and have heart attacks.

I found that with the current Cornish rock cross breed, they are intensely and insanely dumb. Even with access to water, they get really lethargic in the heat and will sit in one place and die instead of going to drink.

Not wanting to invest the time and money (because I couldn't afford either) to purchase bell waterers and hook up another five-gallon bucket to each tractor, I needed water in an emergency.

What I did was buy plastic tubs, one for each tractor, to keep filled with cool water for the chickens to drink. (I got them from the big blue box store and they cost less than $5 a piece.) The tubs are 6" deep and hold about five gallons of water.

I rinse them every day and keep them full of fresh water. This way the birds have the five-gallon bucket with the nipple drinkers and a tub of water to choose from.

Since adding in the tubs of water, I have noticed the birds are really happy. It's not a big deal to fill them as I have a hose run out to the tractors and, most importantly, I have not lost any birds due to the heat.

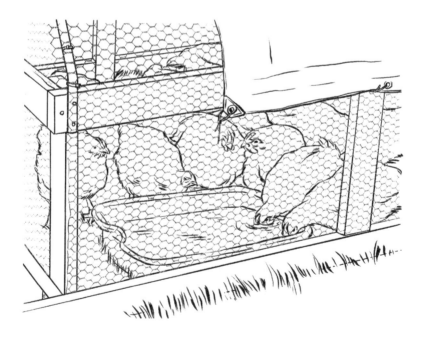

Step 11. Add a Feeder

I decided to go with a trough feeder inside my chicken tractors for a number of reasons.

- Cost-efficiency
- Manure distribution
- Mobility with the tractor (less work)

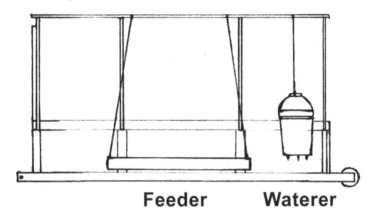

Feeder   Waterer

Design

For these feeders, I went with a 4" schedule 40 PVC pipe with a slit cut into it.

The pipe comes in 10' lengths. First, I cut the pipes in half with a handsaw. This gives you two 5' troughs. It was a little tedious to cut with a handsaw, but it's what I had.

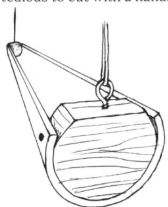

I then put them on the table saw and cut the groves that became the top of the feed trough. My cuts were approximately ⅓ of the pipe apart to give me roughly a 3½" opening. This allows plenty of room for the birds to get their heads in, while leaving a lip so you don't lose much feed to spillage.

I originally tried a cheaper drain pipe with a black center, but found that the plastic was not rugged enough to hold up to both the weight of the feed and the birds stuffing their faces. The schedule 40 pipe, though a few dollars more, is definitely worth it considering the beating these chickens give it come feeding time.

For the ends, I just used a piece of 2" x 4" shaped to fit into the pipe. Once you have all of your cuts made, you can just hold up a piece of 2" x 4" to the end of the pipe and trace your circle.

If you're lucky enough to have a band saw, you can cut the curve all nice and professional-like. I didn't, so I did the best I could with the tools I had. I like the imperfect line as it allows for water to escape, should that become an issue. (It hasn't for me yet and I never lose feed out of those cracks.)

Remember to cut just inside your line. It's easier to compress the pipe onto your block a little than it is to force a larger block into the end of the pipe.

I then attached eye hooks to the 2" x 4" and used ⅛" braided nylon string to suspend the feeders. I tied bowline knots at the feeders to hold them and taut line hitches at the top to be able to adjust the height of the feeders. Adjusting the height is pretty important as the birds age within the tractors.

Other people who have built these chicken tractors have bought 4" PVC caps for the ends of the pipe. You can glue the caps in place and drill a hole through the top of the cap as it sits on the feeder. Then stick a piece of rope through and tie a knot on the end and you have a feeder end. Either option works!

Cost-Effectiveness

I could have bought two ring feeders for each tractor. They are very effective at giving the birds enough space to get their heads into the feeder while fitting many birds around it since they have plenty of room for their big butts to snuggle up next to each other.

The only problem is that I had 12 chicken tractors to build and I didn't want to buy 12 or 24 feeders at a cost of $35-50 per feeder. I needed a solution that wouldn't kill my budget Year One.

That's why I went with the feeder option I chose. It was significantly more cost-effective. It's possible to get a 10' length of schedule 40 pipe for less than $40, which gives me two feeders per pipe, instead of paying that same amount or more for one store-bought feeder.

Manure Distribution

I wanted to create a feeder that would more evenly spread the manure around the footprint of the tractor. I like the trough design because it forces the birds to use most of the chicken tractor as they eat.

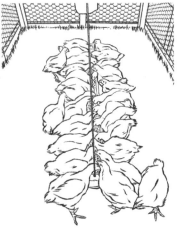

I tried several different placements of the trough. Originally, it was attached to the side of the tractor, but that didn't make sense as the birds only had access to one side.

By placing it in the center of the tractor, the birds have access to both sides, and they can all eat at the same time, even when they get huge and fat. There's still some pushing and shoving, but everyone ends up being fed.

Moving with the Tractor

The feed troughs are suspended in the middle of the tractor, not only so I can adjust the height they sit at, but so they can move with the tractor as well. I don't want to have to walk into the tractor in the morning, take out the trough, move the tractor and replace it.

It is quicker and easier for me to move the tractor with the trough still in it and then scoop feed into the trough while it is still inside.

Restricting Feed, Big Moves and Processing Day

There are certainly times where you want the feed trough out of the way:

- When it comes time for processing day and you are gathering chickens.
- If you choose to remove the trough to restrict their feed at night or the night before they're processed (a big help).
- If you have to move them longer than their typical daily move.

By suspending the troughs from the peak of the arch with some string, I was able to wrap the string around the end of the troughs when I wanted to get them up and out of the way. For this, I recommend having no feed in the troughs, but sometimes you can't avoid it.

Simply wrap the rope around one end of the trough twice. Then repeat the process in the opposing direction with the other side. Keep going until the trough is nestled in the peak of the arch and safely out of your way.

You may be tempted just to get it above the chicken's heads. Even with it out of their way, it still scares them if they can see it swinging around. Get it up to the top and they will forget it is there.

Step 12. Install the Tarp

Installing the tarp is best done with two people to avoid frustration. Also, try not to do this on a windy day, otherwise you're going to be cursing my name and everything that has to do with chicken tractors.

If you were able to find a perfectly sized tarp that measures 10' x 14' feet, then pull the tarp over the tractor and line up all the edges. The 10' side goes front to back and the 14' side goes side to side.

Once the tarp is in place, use the same black zip ties that you used to attach the chicken wire to the conduit to attach the tarp to the chicken tractor. Use the holes in the chicken wire or the conduit itself to anchor the zip ties to the grommets on the tarp.

Getting all four corners secured is a good way to start as it ensures a gust of wind is not going to blow your tarp away. Then go back and put a zip tie at each grommet hole securing it to the chicken tractor.

Step 13. Installing the Wheels

There are two parts to installing the wheels. First, we have to create an axle for them, and then we need to slide the wheels onto that axle before we can move the tractor anywhere.

Start by measuring 1¾" from the back corner of the tractor and 1¾" to the center of the board.

Mark your spot. Drill a ½" hole for the carriage bolt we'll use for the axle.

Insert the bolt and attach half of your 9" strap with two short screws around the bolt. Then put on your washer and nut and tighten everything down.

I add that strap in because it reinforces the carriage bolt for the axle. I did some without it and over time the bolts started to get wiggly in the wood, which was no good.

Personally, even though I have 24 chicken tractors, I only purchased one set of wheels. I simply remove them from one tractor to use on the next during morning chores. It makes life easier since I don't have to keep track of 24 pairs of wheels.

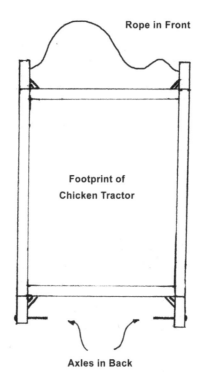

Rope in Front

**Footprint of
Chicken Tractor**

Axles in Back

Step 14. Celebrate one last time!

Your chicken tractor is done!

MOVING PROCESS AND FIELD CHORES

The great thing about raising broilers is that they only take a little time in the morning to move and feed and then you're on with your day.

If you're a homesteader and you only have to move one chicken tractor, then your mornings are going to be easy. If you scale up and move 24, it gets a little rougher, but still manageable, and it is only seasonal so you get a break in the winter.

Honestly, I still enjoy it. There's something cathartic about having a system that's set up and a routine that results in some delicious dinners.

Morning chores for your pastured broilers are going to become routine very quickly and will only vary slightly on a day-to-day basis depending on weather, the bird's age and if anything goes wrong.

I have now moved chicken tractors thousands of times and, after a while, you almost go on autopilot. Since I've had to repeat the process so many times, I've really taken the time to think about the efficiency of my actions feeding, watering and moving the birds every day. That being said, I am constantly looking for ways to improve what I'm doing. I know I can always do a little better.

The daily moves break down into three steps:
- Move
- Feed
- Water

At the end of the morning, if the birds have gotten those things, then you're doing a good job.

I break it down this simply for a good reason. Eventually, you're going to get to the point where you can hire employees or have a friend cover for you so you can take one morning off to sleep in.

If you have the attention to detail that I do (i.e., you're a micro-manager), then you're not going to exactly like how they move your birds. However, stuff the details for a second and think about the three things that the birds are going to need: a move, feed and water. If the person on chores has given the birds that, it's all good.

Tractor Alignment: Diagonal vs. Straight

All the photos of Joel Salatin's chicken tractors has them offset and in a diagonal line. I cannot tell you how jealous that makes me. No joke. I bet the moves are a little easier to line up and allows for a little more margin for error in the daily pulls.

I line my chicken tractors up in a straight line for some very specific reasons.

I line them up straight because of predators. Even with a solidly built chicken tractor, there is still the possibility of something ripping through the mesh, something digging under it, or something just plain barging in.

I have had a bobcat rip apart chicken wire to get into a chicken tractor before. She ripped a hole in the side and killed all the birds inside.

With the tractors in a line, fewer of the sides of each tractor are exposed making it more secure and giving the birds an area they can run to that a predator cannot reach as easily.

I also string a single strand of electric fence wire around the entire set of tractors. This is positioned 6" out from the edge of the chicken tractor and 6" above the ground. My theory is that nothing can stand and dig under the tractor or get into the side without hitting the electric wiring. It is exactly where a raccoon or bobcat would have to put its body if it was trying to reach in with its grubby little paws.

Since instituting the electric wire, I have not had any issues with critters injuring or killing my birds.

I also line the chicken tractors up for land efficiency. To use the Joel Salatin comparison again, if you were to travel in a diagonal line across your pasture, there's a little triangle of unused space at either end where one end of the diagonal never reaches. That's all well and good if you have other livestock to graze or you have enough space where it's okay to let that land go unused, but I don't have a lot of acres that are suitable for broiler chickens. Depending on the time of year and how wet it is, I actually have limited land to use for broilers. I have to make the most out of what I have.

Arranging the chicken tractors in a line, for me, uses the space I have most efficiently. Not every rotation works perfectly with the amount of space I might need or use, but I'm doing alright so far.

Move

Moving the birds to a new location before doing your other chores ensures that you're not walking through manure when you go into the chicken tractors to feed the birds.

As far as the birds are concerned, though, getting the birds on new grass encourages them to eat the grass and bugs before they step and poop all over the place and before they fill up on grain.

It also gets the hard work out of the way so that the rest of it is easier by comparison.

Before I move the chickens, I put on a pair of rubber-dipped gloves. They're inexpensive and they keep the poop from getting under your fingernails. As you move the chicken tractors forward, the wheels are going to roll over the manure that's there and it will cake up on the wheels a bit.

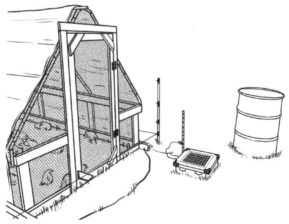

The gloves keep your hands clean. If you're not the type of person who loves grabbing poo-covered wheels with your bare hands, they're a cheap investment and well worth it.

To move the chicken tractors, I start by taking down the electric fence in front of the tractors. I just pull it back instead of taking the time to put it on a reel. There's no benefit to taking extra time to mess with a reel. If you're careful about how you pull it back, it won't tangle and it will be quicker and easier than taking the time to spin a plastic wheel.

The fence behind the tractors, I just leave alone because, after they're all moved, I'll move the fence up to meet the tractors. That means that I don't have to wind the fence. It doesn't get tangled and I don't have to hang it on the posts again.

Anything you can do to cut seconds of time on a daily basis makes your birds more profitable. Not rolling up the electric wire or even finding a way to do it without electric fencing means that you invest fewer labor hours into your birds, which means more money in your pocket.

After the fence is down, I pick an end, usually where I ended the day before because the wheels are there. I put the wheels on the back of the tractors one at a time and then walk around to the front. At the front I bend my knees, pick up the rope that lifts the front of the chicken tractor, lift the tractor off the ground, lean backward and pull the tractor with me.

After you move the tractor, being careful not to crush any birds, set it down, walk around back, take the wheels off to move to the next chicken tractor. Here are the steps:

1. Fence down and moved from in front of birds.
2. Wheels on first tractor.
3. Move and carefully line up first tractor.
4. Wheels off and move to next chicken tractor.
5. Finish and celebrate.

Feed

My feed comes in 50 lb bags on one-ton pallets. That's 40 bags that are 50 lbs each. That is in part because I don't have the infrastructure to deal with bulk feed and partly because my feed mill doesn't currently offer bulk feed. While it comes in 50 lb bags, I don't want to deal with those bags every single day.

This is one of those areas of the farm that I continue to work on—not only reducing how many times feed gets moved on my farm, but how many times I actually have to lift feed using only manpower.

Moving chicken tractors and hauling feed are two physically intense chores that wear you down the larger your operation gets, unless you change the way you do business. I want to raise chickens forever, but I sure as heck don't want to do all the lifting forever. My body just won't be able to handle it.

In the field with each set of chickens lives a black steel barrel. Those barrels hold up to 325 lbs of broiler grower mash. Considering my feeders can hold roughly 75 lbs of feed all together, that means that when I'm refilling an empty barrel some morning during chores, I can bring out 400 lbs of feed in one trip.

In the black barrel, I keep a five-gallon bucket and a three-quart feed scoop. When the grain is stored in the barrel, I use the bucket and scoop to dole the feed out to the birds.

The bucket has a handle and only holds about 25 lbs, so it's more manageable than trying to lug around a feed bag. I use a three-quart scoop because it is more shallow and fits inside the five-gallon bucket no matter what way you spin it. That's helpful when you are getting toward the bottom of the bucket and you're scooping grain out.

I simply fill up my bucket with feed and walk it out to the chicken tractors. Depending on their age, I can fill 2 to

3 feeders with a full bucket of feed. That's 2 to 3 trips to the barrel for an eight-tractor batch of birds.

Water

As mentioned earlier, for watering, I have five-gallon buckets with nipple drinkers that hang at the back of the chicken tractor. When the birds get to weeks 7 and 8, I add a watering tub to give them more access to water. I don't use them when the birds are smaller because it's an open tub and the birds could get stuck and drown.

The buckets and tubs travel along with the tractor when I move it–the buckets because they're suspended and the tubs because the lip catches on the chicken tractor and it gets pushed along the grass. After the move and while I'm feeding, I may empty the tub or the bucket if the water is looking less than clear and refill it with my garden hose after I'm done feeding.

To water, I keep a hose run out to each and every batch of chicken tractors on pasture, because I can. I have hundreds of feet of garden hose and a very good well. I also have strategic pasture locations where a hose can reach a water source and a batch of birds. So I've planned my rotations partly on that system.

Life wasn't always this luxurious. In the beginning, on my first farm, my birds were far away from my water source. Because of that, I would fill five-gallon buckets and put them in the back of my SUV. I would then drive those five-gallon buckets of water every day out to water my birds.

Nowadays I can move, add and subtract hose as necessary. It was such a big step up from carting buckets around that I hadn't revisited the system in a while. Now that I have a few years farming with this system, I'm starting to price out and explore the logistics of a more permanent system—something where I can attach and detach the tractors with quick disconnects, there's constant fresh water, and it's as easy to move as everything else is.

There are a few members of the American Pastured Poultry Producers Association (APPPA) that have been working on similar projects and I'm excited to dig into it more with them.

Time

All this talk about efficiency and here I am about to tell you to slow down a little bit and take a second to look at your birds.

I constantly look for ways to save time when it comes to work. The less time I spend doing the things that I *have* to do, the more time I can spend on the things I *want* to do.

I want to sit and watch my birds and take pictures or video because that's what I enjoy. Standing there with a hose in my hand or lugging feed doesn't carry the same sense of satisfaction on a daily basis.

Taking some time to sit and observe your chickens is a good and valuable thing. Observation is when you notice sickness, behavior and nuances that make you a better poultry farmer. You'll start to pick up on subtle behavioral patterns. The better you know your chickens, the more likely you will be able to make decisions that positively affect their lives.

PREDATORS

I have encountered many types of predators with my chicken tractors–by land, by air and, well, not yet by sea.

The tractors have stood the test and I have learned some lessons along the way. There were a few injuries to my birds, but my mistakes are your gains. With any luck, you will not have to go through what I did.

Bobcat, that's right, bobcat. There is a bobcat that lives in the backwoods of my property that I have seen in person a couple times during the day and examples of her work during the night. This gal tried on several occasions to get into the chicken tractors.

The new design worked the way it should. I could see pulls on the chicken wire, but not breaks and no entry. The birds were a little freaked, but they all lived without injury. That's where it pays to use the pneumatic stapler instead of the hand-held staple gun, if you can. The pneumatic staples go in a little deeper and hold up a lot nicer.

On this same note, there are a lot of coyotes, foxes and other predators in my area. With the electric wire and the chicken tractors combined I haven't had an issue where any catastrophic loss has occurred.

Aerial predators are not a problem. With the chicken trac-tors fully covered in chicken wire and tarp, there is no way for an aerial predator to get in. I have seen hawks crash into the side of the chicken tractors before, no joke, but they have never gotten in.

We have seen bear in the neighborhood and, man, am I glad I wasn't around when this guy came traipsing through. Honestly, I think if a bear really wanted to get in, it could. If you ever see a grown bear in person, you'd understand. They're huge, they're pure muscle, and they do whatever they want.

Predators will inevitably be a part of raising chickens. Once you have birds on your farm, everyone in the neighbor-hood knows and they will come to visit. Do the best for your birds, but know that sh** happens when something smarter and more determined than you breaks through and you lose some beloved chickens. You will continue to learn, adjust your system and hopefully, over time, predators will not be an issue.

FUTURE FEEDING EXPERIMENTS

One of the good and bad things about entrepreneurial life is that you never really believe anything is finished. On the one hand, it's obnoxious because you're always working on something to make it better. On the other hand, things get better.

There are conflicting schools of thought on restricting feed for broilers of certain breeds in order to let their organs and bones catch up to how fast they put on meat.

Full-grown birds will eat all the feed in these troughs before 24 hours are up. It's your decision whether you feed them twice a day or you let them go without for a few hours to let their bodies grow.

I will be doing more experimenting with my feed since it's the greatest expense in raising broilers. That means it merits some analysis.

What if I put in higher capacity feeders? Could that cut down on my labor? Does it make the tractors too heavy? What would be a good size so that I get maximum benefit without adding in too much weight?

What are the consequences on the birds through all of this? With no breaks in their feed, will I get the same size birds in less time? Will my mortality rates go up if I go to full feed or will their life on pasture offset their added gain?

All these questions, and then there's the local adaptation to my farm, the time of year, the hatchery that I use, etc...

It's daunting at times thinking of all the factors that can go into farming. At the end of the day, I enjoy the process and I love that no matter how much you think you know, there is always room for improvement.

I hope as you experiment with raising chickens of your own, you find the same sense of pleasure and accomplishment that I have!

ABOUT THE AUTHOR

As of the rewrite of this book in 2016, I live and work on a 52-acre farm in Western Connecticut. My main operation has always been pastured broilers, however, through the years I have expanded to pigs, sheep, hops, apples, herbs and vegetables. My farm, Camps Road Farm, is one part of a three-part business that includes Kent Falls Brewing Co., a farm brewery on property, and Neversink Spirits, a craft distillery off property.

Since getting into farming, I have raised as few as 40 broilers and as many as 2,400 broilers in one season. No matter what else I end up growing on my farm, chickens always seem to maintain a special place in my heart. They're enjoyable to raise, my community loves them, and they're a vital part of the success of my farm.

My life has taken a lot of interesting turns. I grew up in Connecticut and went to college at the University of Connecticut as a technical theater major. After school, I moved to New York City where I worked for four years in scenic and lighting design, primarily for television.

After getting sick of city life, my wife, Kate, and I decided to ride our bicycles 5,500 miles across the United States visiting farms and craft breweries along the way. After a year of purposeful homelessness, we landed back in CT to apprentice on a farm for a season and eventually start our own broiler operation.

Somewhere along the way, I started Farm Marketing Solutions, my multimedia publishing company, with the goal of educating and inspiring the next generation of farmers. Drawing from my media background, I wanted to share my story with others in the hopes that more people will decide to homestead or choose farming as a career.

I love what I do every day. I have found pleasure and fulfillment in farming that I hadn't thought possible to achieve in the working world. On a regular basis, I get to create life and then share that experience with others. I grow food that is not only good for people, but good for the planet. It's friggin' great!

My hope with this book is that you come to find the same joy as I have in purposeful food. Chickens were meant to live on grass, not in barns. With every chicken tractor book sold, we're one step closer to a society that appreciates chickens as much as I do.

Farm Marketing Solutions

To follow along with my activity on Camps Road Farm and get more interesting farming information, head to the website, FarmMarketingSolutions.com. You may want to check out the Book Shelf on the site for recommendations of my favorite farm-related books, including Joel Salatin's *Pastured Poultry Profit$*.

You can also see frequent updates on my YouTube channel at youtube.com/FarmMarketing.

I love to see people applying the information I provided in this book, so please feel free to share your stories, photos and videos by sending an email to Hello@FarmMarketingSolutions.com.

Thank You!

I wanted to take a second and thank you for purchasing my book. Any and all proceeds from the book go to support my family, my work with Farm Marketing Solutions, and my farm. They thank you as well.

I also wanted to thank...

...my family for their unfailing support with all my crazy endeavors.

...Scott Messina, my business partner at Farm Marketing Solutions, for everything he does for the business, including editing my written streams of consciousness.

...Dan Hamilton for his help creating the illustrations that were too hard for me to draw.

...Mike Marques for making me look good in my author photos.

...Tara Alemany and Emerald Lake Books for their help formatting the book, publishing it and making me at least seem professional.

...Troy Bishopp the Grass Whisperer for teaching me how to be a better farmer.

...Camps Road Farm and The Food Cycle, LLC, for supporting their farm manager in many different ways.

And many thanks to everyone who provided feedback on the first edition and made this book that much better:

Harry Allbright
Mike Bott of Antler Acres
Bob Buhler of Prairie Serenity Farm
Roger Chi
Robert Coulter of Peak View Farm

R. Daniel

Jason Draper

Diane Edwards

Adrienne Hurd

Patrick Kalmes

Amber Kenyon of Greener Pastures Ranching

Kevin Krause

Chris Kyger of C&C Farms

James Mac

Ron McConnnell

Bradley Moggach of Farm Craft Organics

Sean Montague

Nour Mouktabis of Amana Ranch

Erin Patoine

Travis Redman

Don Scroggins of Hickory Valley Farm

Christopher Taggart

Dean Yeo of Little D Farm

CUTTING PARTS AND DIAGRAM SUMMARY

The following four pages are a summary of the cutting lists found on pages 35-36 and 40-41.

Cutting List

Part A: Cut one 2" x 4" x 8' board into four 2' sections.

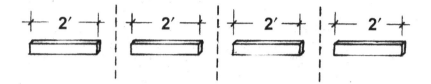

Part B: Cut another 2" x 4" x 8' board into four 2' sections.

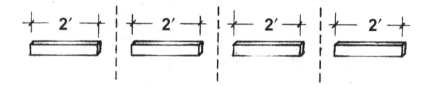

Part C: Cut one 2" x 4" x 12' board into two sections, both 5' 7" long.

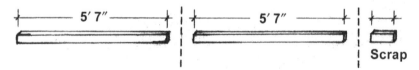

Part D: Just leave two 2" x 4" x 10' boards whole.

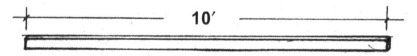

Part E: Cut two of your 2" x 4" x 12' boards into 11' 4" lengths.

Parts F & G: Cut one 2" x 4" x 10' board into one section 5' 7" long and cut two sections 1' 9⅜" long.

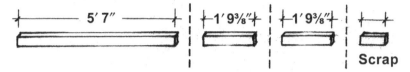

Parts I & J: Cut two 1" x 4" x 8' boards into one section 4' 8½" long and one more section 2' long.

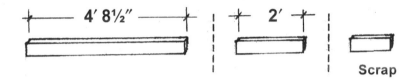

Parts K & L: Cut two 1" x 4" x 8' board into one 5' section and one more section 2' 7¼" long.

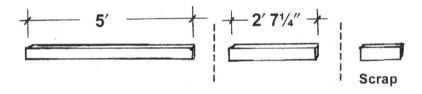

Half-Lap Joint Cutting List

Part A: x 4

Part D: x 2

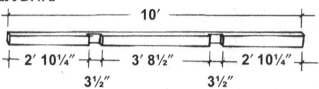

Part E: x 2

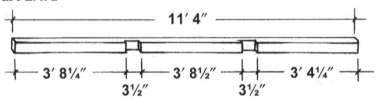

Part F: x 1

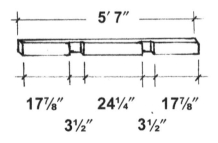

Part G: x 2

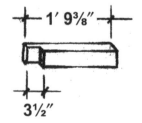

Putting It All Together

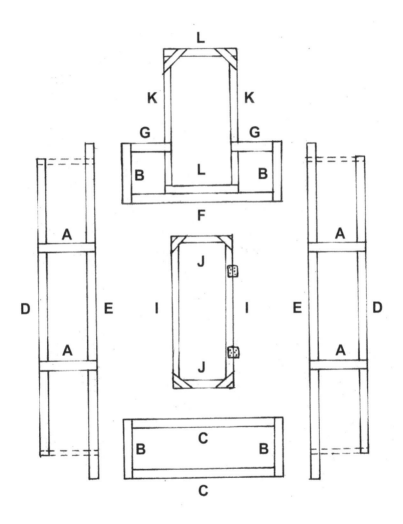

YOUR NOTES

YOUR NOTES

MORE RESOURCES FROM

As fast as information travels these days, it's important to stay current. Rather than continually updating this book, you can check this web page for additional information and resources:

FarmMarketingSolutions.com/resources/broilers

Included are:
  Links to favorite poultry books
  Links to useful resources
  More videos from the farm
  Free PDF downloads on:
    • Troubleshooting disease
    • Forage trials
    • All-natural water additive trials
    • ... and more!

Farm Marketing Solutions started because I wanted a place to log all the research and progress I have made throughout the years. Now we can both benefit by having an organized list of useful resources from a person who is actually farming for a living.

1 MILLION CHICKENS INITIATIVE

*I got into pasture-based systems
for the politics
and I stayed for dinner.*

It is my life's goal to feed people healthy and delicious food. Growing chickens on grass gives you the most delicious bird you have ever eaten.

Not only do I want to supply my CSA and farmers' market customers with the best chicken ever, I want people all over the world to taste how good this chicken is. I cannot do that alone. What I am proposing is to have you grow chickens with me to help me reach my goal.

How am I going to calculate this? Assume that anyone who buys my book, *Stress-Free Chicken Tractor Plans*, is going to build at least one chicken tractor. If each chicken tractor comfortably raises 25 broiler chickens, with enough of us we can hit one million chickens in no time.

Real change comes by many people doing simple acts. Raising chickens for meat can be enjoyable, profitable and delicious.

*It's time we spread the message about chicken
that actually tastes like chicken.*

Visit
FarmMarketingSolutions.com
for more info.

1 BOOK

+

1 CHICKEN TRACTOR

---

25 CHICKENS

8-WEEK VIDEO SERIES
RAISING BROILER CHICKENS FROM START TO FINISH

Anyone can raise broiler chickens on grass!

Grow all the chicken you need for a year or add a profitable pastured poultry enterprise to your farm. Throughout this 8-week series, John shows you the process of growing, slaughtering and cooking your pasture-raised chicken.

Follow along from the brooder to the processor as John shows you what it's like to raise chicken for meat.

All the birds were brooded together and then separated to raise one full production batch of 240 birds on pasture and a smaller homestead batch of 25 birds in John's front yard.

Every day, video was recorded to track their progress and posted at the end of the week. Comments and questions on related topics were answered in each.

• Chicks Arrive • Life in the Brooder
• Chicks Move Out to Grass • Fields Chores
• Let Them Eat Grass • Feeding Grain
• Why Do This? • Processing

All episodes can be found here:
FarmMarketingSolutions.com/raising-chickens-for-meat

FARM MARKETING SOLUTIONS
400 VIDEOS
AND COUNTING!

Shaped as much by what you want to see as what John chooses to shoot.

Experimentation, iteration, exploration and, finally, sharing with you the successes and failures found on a farm.

Farm operations are covered in depth.

You'll find videos on:

- Raising pastured broilers
- Raising pastured pigs
- Raising egg-layers on pasture
- Beginning a hopyard and apple orchard
- Starting and growing your farm business
- Farm equipment
- ...and more!

Subscribe at
YouTube.com/FarmMarketing

LIFE IS A JOURNEY
FARMING IS A LIFESTYLE

In this podcast, John crowdsources the education he's gained over several years of farming, asking local farmer friends for help or cold-calling strangers all over the country. One certain thing:

*There is always more
to experience and learn.*

New episodes are released as time and energy allows within a farmer's schedule!

FarmMarketingSolutions.com/growingfarmspodcast

Past Topics

- Is a Homesteader Considered a Farmer
- Farm Location and Branding Make All the Difference
- Farm Planning and Execution
- Multiple Income Streams from One Product
- Farmers Using Instagram
- Commercial Kitchen on a Farm
- 5 Lessons Learned on the Farm this Year

Conversations with Guests

- Raising Chickens
- Raising Pigs
- Setting Up Your Farmers' Market Stand
- How to Leverage Social Media as a Farmer
- How to Manage Employees
- How to Start a Farm at School
- How the Business Side of Farming Works
- How a Book can be a Great Farm Marketing Tool

**Available on iTunes
or wherever you listen to podcasts.
Already a listener? Please leave a review!**

Are You Thinking of Growing Your Pastured Broiler Operation?

Take the guesswork out of planning, tracking and assessing what you're doing when you put a chicken on grass and then try to sell it!

FARM MARKETING SOLUTIONS
PASTURED POULTRY PACKET

Everything you need to start and grow your pastured poultry operation.

Shorten your learning curve and get the right systems in place the first time with this complete collection of resources.

COVERS TWO CATEGORIES:

INFRASTRUCTURE and BUSINESS
• Profitability breakdown • Infrastructure planning
• Examples of rotations at different scales
• Pasture requirements • Value stream mapping
• Tracking sheets • Brooder & pasture checklists

MARKETING and SALES
• Chicken CSA model explained • Infographics to help you sell
• Email marketing strategies • Examples of flyers
• Tips for selling to customers • Tips for your website

Visit **FarmMarketingSolutions.com**
for this and more broiler resources.

The Pastured Poultry Packet is sold as a digital download.

FARM MARKETING SOLUTIONS
BROILER VIDEO COURSE

Following the 8-week series,
you wanted more details.

If a successful business is your goal, there are many things you can do to make your experience more enjoyable, to raise healthier birds, and to make more profit. But the devil is in the details!

This video course on raising broilers will be available in December 2017.

Sign up to be notified of this
course's progress and release date.

Topics Covered

- Planning your farm infrastructure
- Getting ready for chicks
- Success in the brooder
- Raising chickens on pasture
- Processing chickens for home and sale
- Starting a chicken CSA
- Incorporating broilers into your homestead or existing farm
- Discussing pastured poultry with customers

More information can be found here:
FarmMarketingSolutions.com/broiler-video-course

Visit us at
emeraldlakebooks.com

Made in USA - Kendallville, IN
66031_9780996567480